Sad Simon

Louise Tribble

Illustrated by Rhiannon Thomas

Dedicated to all of Millie's friends.

Sad Simon

Louise Tribble

Illustrated by Rhiannon Thomas

This is Simon.

Simon is feeling sad.

We all feel sad sometimes but some of us feel sad a lot of the time.

Sometimes we don't feel like playing or seeing friends.

Sometimes all we want to do is sit and watch telly even when our friends want us to play.

Sometimes we just want to sleep and sometimes we can't sleep at all.

Sometimes all we want to do is eat and sometimes we don't feel like eating at all.

It's very important to tell family and friends how we feel.

Simon is ringing his friend Millie to tell her how he is feeling.

It is important we listen to how our friends feel too.

"We can get through this together," said Millie.

"Thank you, Millie," said Simon.

"What makes you happy?" Millie asks Simon.

"I like painting, baking, reading, and gardening," said Simon.

What do you like to do?

You could draw pictures of your favourite things to do and put them next to Simon's pictures!

Millie and Simon are spending some time doing things that make Simon happy.

What have you done today that has made you happy?

Millie is teaching Simon how to be Mindful and live in the moment.

"Look at this flower, Simon. What colour is it? Does it smell?" Millie asks.

Mindfulness can also help you to describe how you feel, which can be hard because sometimes we don't know how we feel.

"Shall we do a bodyscan, Simon?" asks Millie.

"It will help you to stay in the moment and notice how you are feeling. We will do this slowly so you have a chance to notice," said Millie.

"Lie down with a blanket as you might get cold. Close your eyes. Notice any feelings in your toes. How do your feet feel? Notice any feelings in your legs. Notice how your back feels. It doesn't matter if you don't feel anything. How does your tummy feel? Notice any feelings in your chest and shoulders. How do your arms feel? Notice any feelings in your neck, your head, and your face."

"Work your way back down to your feet. You might feel tingling, aches or nothing at all - and anything is fine," said Millie.

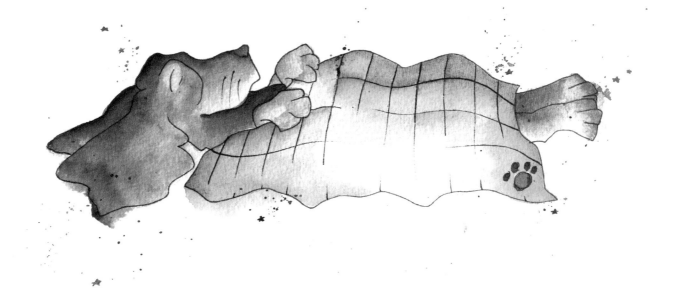

"Thank you for a wonderful day, Millie. I'm feeling much better," said Simon.

Sad Simon is all about a young Bassett Hound.
Like all of us, he sometimes feels sad. Simon explains that for some the sadness can last for longer and have a bigger effect on life. Luckily he gets in touch with his friend Mindful Millie who helps to teach him ways to use Mindfulness to feel better. Join Millie and Simon with your children and we can build a positive future together.

Millie the elephant lives life in the present, she uses Mindfulness to capture every moment and to help others by teaching them techniques to build a positive mental health. You can read about Millie in her book 'Mindful Millie'.

ISBN: 978-1-9997948-2-8

Printed in Poland
by Amazon Fulfillment
Poland Sp. z o.o., Wrocław